Broken for you

**A Mass setting for congregation
with optional choir and instrumental parts**

Margaret **Rizza**

We hope you enjoy *Broken for you*. Further copies are available
from your local Kevin Mayhew stockist.

In case of difficulty, please contact the publisher direct by writing to:

The Sales Department
KEVIN MAYHEW LTD
Buxhall
Stowmarket
Suffolk IP14 3BW

Phone 01449 737978
Fax 01449 737834
E-mail info@kevinmayhewltd.com

Please ask for our complete catalogue of outstanding Church Music.

First published in Great Britain in 2001 by Kevin Mayhew Ltd.

© Copyright 2001 Kevin Mayhew Ltd.

ISBN 1 84003 777 6
ISMN M 57004 900 4
Catalogue No: 1450222

0 1 2 3 4 5 6 7 8 9

Cover design by Jonathan Stroulger

Music setter: Geoffrey Moore
Proof reader: Marian Hellen

Printed and bound in Great Britain

Foreword

This setting may be performed by whatever voices and instruments you have available.

It can be sung in unison or with a choir, accompanied by organ alone or any number of instruments.

The congregation (for whom a photocopiable part is given on page 61) sing the melody throughout except in one or two places which are indicated in the score.

We would like to thank the following people for their performances on the enclosed CD:

Voices

Honor Mason	Soprano solo
Diana Campbell	Alto solo
Mark Holmes	Baritone solo
Paul Plumbley	Speaker
St Thomas' Music Group	

Instrumentalists

Ian Davies	Flute
Daniel Weatherley	Violin
Nancy Sergeant	Oboe
Catharine Brooker	Cello
Paul Dean	Organ

Conducted by Margaret Rizza

Recorded in St Thomas' Church, Sevenoaks, Kent, by B&H Sound Services Ltd.

Please photocopy this page

KEVIN MAYHEW EASY COPYRIGHT CLEARANCE

The setting in this book is copyright and must not be reproduced in any way without the proper permission.

A one-year licence to reproduce the **congregational part only** (pages 61-64) of *Broken for you* (*Cat. no. 1450222*) for non-commercial use may be obtained from the Kevin Mayhew Copyright Department by sending a copy of this page together with your payment.

Name of Church _____

Contact Name _____

Address _____

_____

Postcode _____

Telephone Number _____ **Fax Number** _____

E-mail _____

Fee for one-year licence: £10.58.

This fee is valid until 31 December 2002. After that date please contact the Copyright Department for information.

Please enclose payment by cheque or fill in the details of your Visa/Mastercard number below.

Expiry date until end _____

Signed _____

To be completed by Kevin Mayhew Ltd

Payment of £10.58 received. Thank you.

Permission is granted subject to the following further conditions:

1. that the composers are acknowledged on every copy.

2. that the following copyright line is included on every copy:

    Copyright Kevin Mayhew Ltd. Reproduced by permission from *Broken for you (Cat. no. 1450222)*

    Licence Number _____ Licence expires on: _____

Signed for Kevin Mayhew Ltd _____

Copyright Department, Kevin Mayhew Ltd, Buxhall, Stowmarket, Suffolk, IP14 3BW
Telephone number: UK 01449 737978   International +44 1449 737978
Fax number: UK 01449 737834   International +44 1449 737834
                E-mail: info@kevinmayhewltd.com

for St Thomas' Music Group

BROKEN FOR YOU

A Mass setting for congregation
with optional choir and instrumental parts

Margaret Rizza

KYRIE

** Small notes to be played only
if there is no solo instrument.*

KYRIE

Cello (Basso Continuo)

KYRIE

GLORIA

Glo - ry to God in the high - est, glo - ry to God on high; and

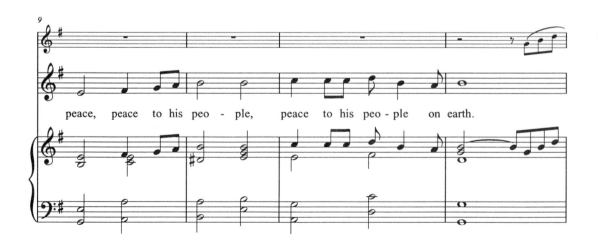

peace, peace to his peo - ple, peace to his peo - ple on earth.

Lord God, hea - ven - ly King, al - migh - ty God and

Fa - ther, we wor - ship you, we give you thanks, we

praise you for your glo - ry. Glo - ry to God in the

high - est and peace to his peo - ple on earth.

Lord Je-sus Christ, on-ly Son of the Fa - ther, Lord God, Lamb of God,

you take a-way the sin of the world, have mer - cy, have mer-cy on us.

You are seat-ed at the right hand of the Fa-ther, re-ceive our prayer, re-

You are seat-ed at the right hand of the Fa-ther, re-ceive our prayer, re-

ceive our prayer.

ceive our prayer.

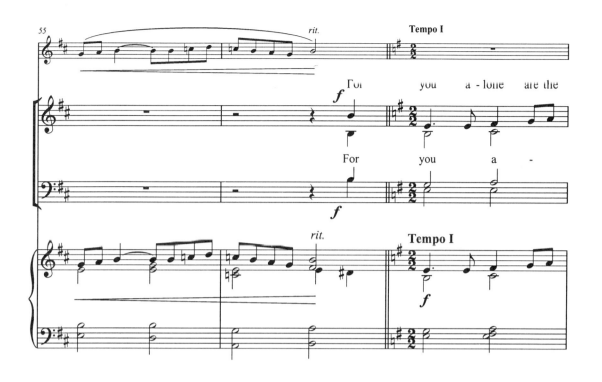

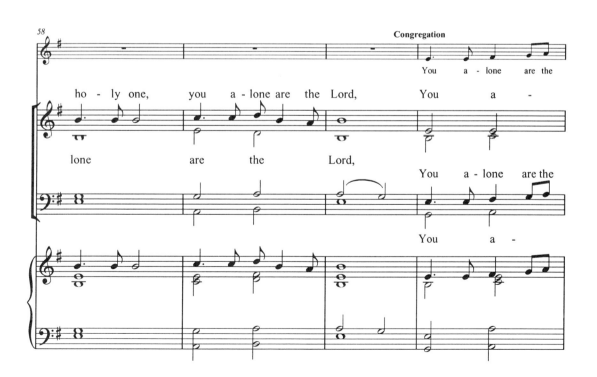

15

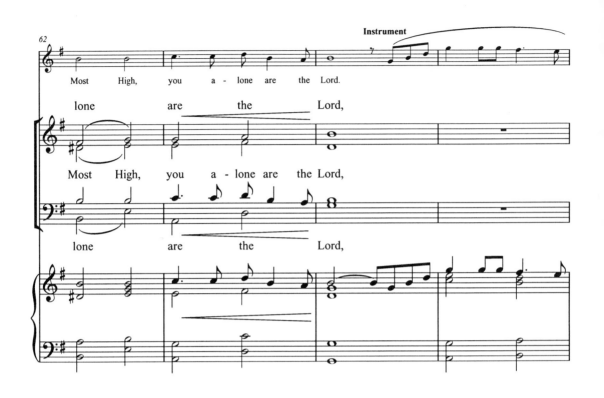

Christ with the Ho - ly Spi - rit, in the

glo - ry, the glo - ry, the glo - ry of the

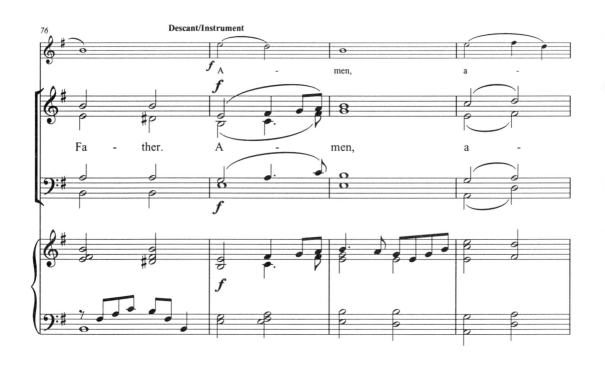

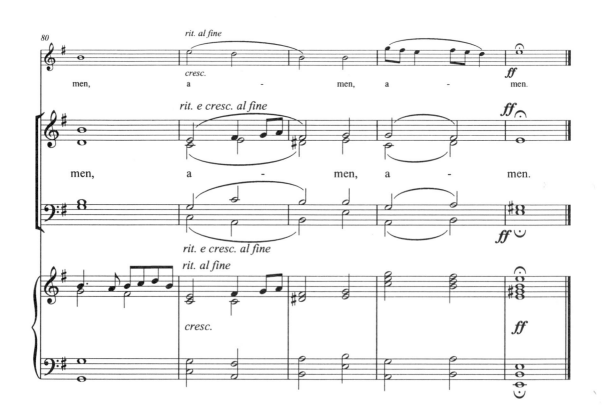

GLORIA

GLORIA

Cello (Basso Continuo)

GOSPEL ACCLAMATION

Al - le - lu - ia, al - le - lu - ia,

al - le - lu - ia, al - le - lu - ia.

Verse. Example I

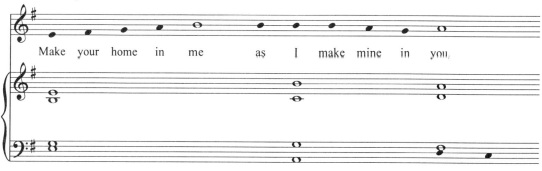

Make your home in me as I make mine in you,

who - e - ver re - mains in me bears fruit in plen - ty.

Verse. Example II

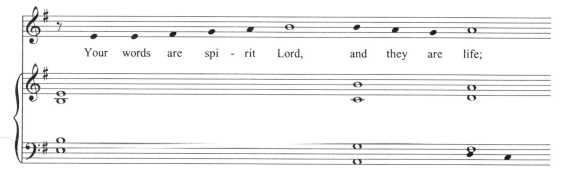

Your words are spi - rit Lord, and they are life;

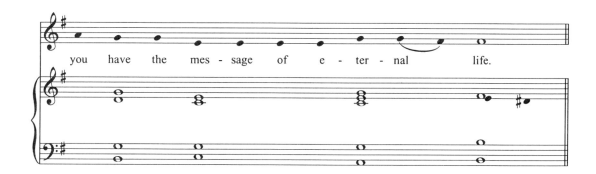

you have the mes - sage of e - ter - nal life.

OPTIONAL CODA

GOSPEL ACCLAMATION

* *A verse follows the first 12 bars, immediately preceding the instrumental entry.*

GOSPEL ACCLAMATION

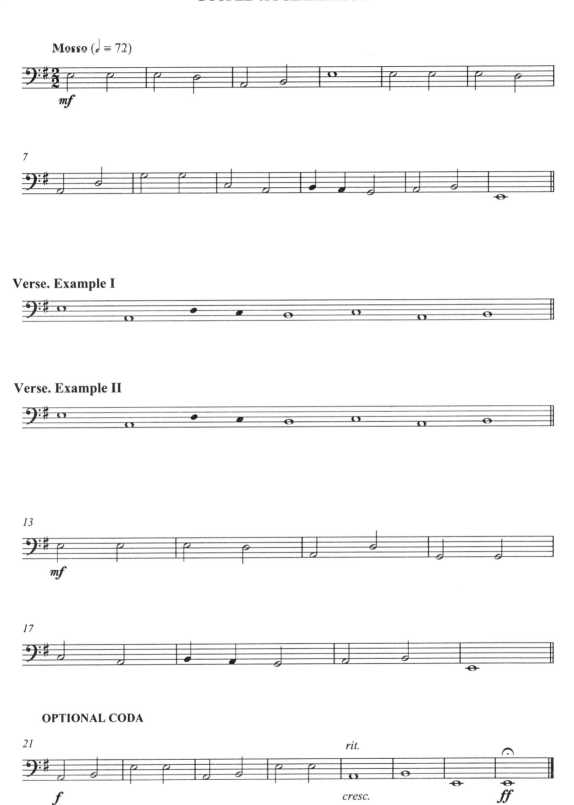

SANCTUS

31

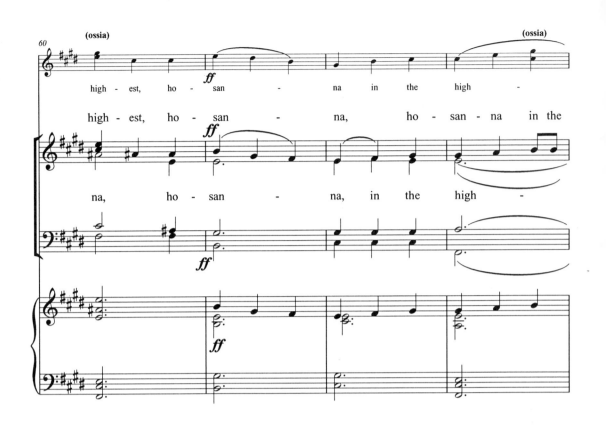

SANCTUS

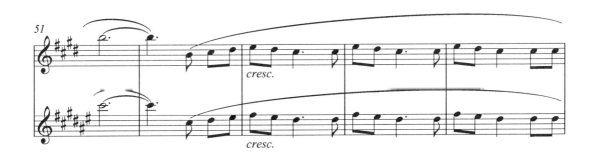

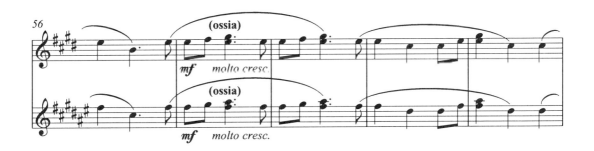

Cello (Basso Continuo)

SANCTUS

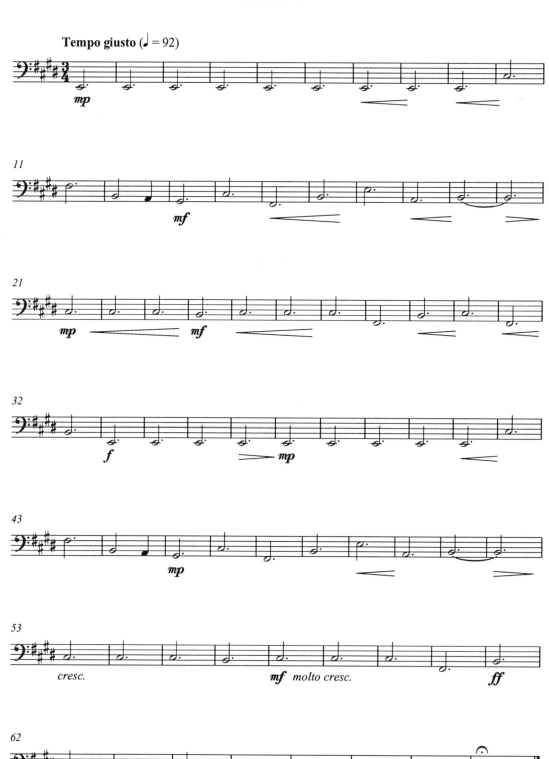

ACCLAMATIONS
1

2

Cello (Basso Continuo)

ACCLAMATIONS
1, 2 and 4

Tempo giusto

3

Tempo giusto

DOXOLOGY AND GREAT AMEN

Traditional Doxology
Celebrant

Through him, with him, in him, in the u-ni-ty of the Ho-ly Spi-rit,

all glo-ry and hon-our is yours, al-migh-ty Fa-ther, for e-ver and e-ver.

Alternative Doxology
Celebrant
Con moto

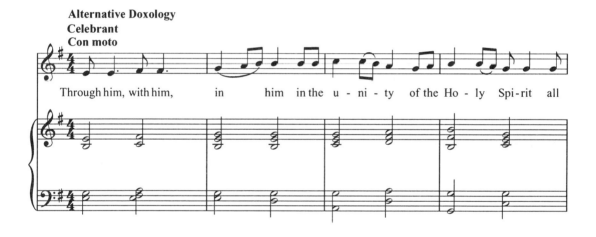

Through him, with him, in him in the u-ni-ty of the Ho-ly Spi-rit all

glo-ry and hon-our is yours al-migh-ty Fa-ther for e-ver, for e-ver and e-ver.

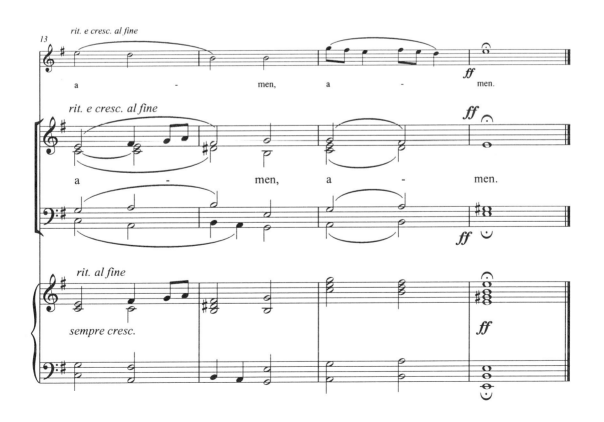

DOXOLOGY AND GREAT AMEN

Traditional Doxology (unaccompanied)

Alternative Doxology

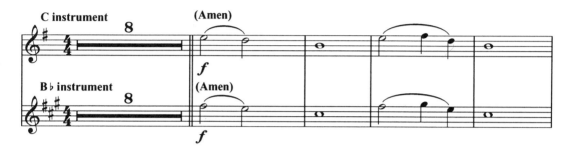

Cello (Basso Continuo)

DOXOLOGY AND GREAT AMEN

Traditional Doxology (unaccompanied)

Alternative Doxology

Amen

OUR FATHER

Throughout this setting the words 'Holy be thy name' are sung by the choir alone.
They do not appear in the congregation's part.

And lead us not in-to temp-ta-tion; hal-lowed be thy name:

ho - ly be thy name. But de - li - ver us from e - vil,

de - li - ver us from e - vil. Hal - lowed be thy name.

Celebrant: Deliver us, Lord, from every evil, and grant us peace in our day.
In your mercy keep us free from sin and protect us from all anxiety
as we wait in joyful hope for the coming of our Saviour, Jesus Christ.

To be played very quietly while the above is said.

For the king-dom, the pow'r and the glo - ry are yours now and for e - ver.

OUR FATHER

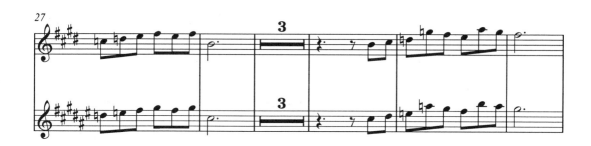

Celebrant: Deliver us, Lord, from every evil, and grant us peace in our day. In your mercy keep us free from sin and protect us from all anxiety as we wait in joyful hope for the coming of our Saviour, Jesus Christ.

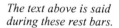

The text above is said during these rest bars.

Cello (Basso Continuo)

OUR FATHER

Celebrant: Deliver us, Lord, from every evil, and grant us peace in our day.
In your mercy keep us free from sin and protect us from all anxiety
as we wait in joyful hope for the coming of our Saviour, Jesus Christ.

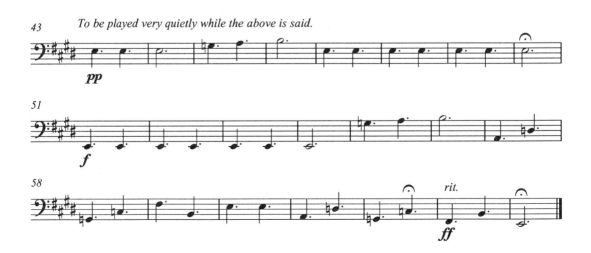

AGNUS DEI

to be played when there is no solo instrument

Accompaniment with instrument

Accompaniment without instrument

AGNUS DEI

AGNUS DEI

Calmly and prayerfully (♩ = 60)

25 **Accompaniment with melody instrument**

25 **Accompaniment without melody instrument**

BROKEN FOR YOU

Margaret Rizza

Spi - rit, in the glo - ry, the glo - ry, the glo - ry of the Fa - ther.

A - men, a - men, a - men, a - men.

GOSPEL ACCLAMATION

Mosso (♩ = 72)

Al - le - lu - ia, al - le - lu - ia, al - le - lu - ia, al - le - lu - ia.

Verse. Example I

Make your home in me as I make mine in you, who - e - ver re - mains in me bears fruit in plen - ty.

Verse. Example II

Your words are spi - rit Lord, and they are life; you have the mes - sage of e - ter - nal life.

Al - le - lu - ia, al - le - lu - ia, al - le - lu - ia, al - le - lu - ia.

OPTIONAL CODA

Al - le - lu - ia, al - le - lu - ia, al - le - lu - ia.

SANCTUS

Tempo giusto (♩ = 92)

Men

Ho - ly, ho - ly, ho - ly Lord, God of pow'r and God of might; hea - ven and earth are

Women

full of your glo - ry, are full of your glo - ry. Ho - san - na, ho - san - na, ho - san - na in the high - est; ho-

ACCLAMATIONS

1

san - na, ho - san - na, ho - san - na in the high - est, ho - san - na, ho - san - na in the high - est.

Women
Bles-sed, bles-sed, bles-sed is he, he who comes in the name of the Lord. Bles-sed is he who comes in the name, who

comes in the name of the Lord. Ho - san - na, ho - san - na, ho - san - na in the high - est; ho - san - na, ho -

san - na, ho - san - na in the high - est, ho - san - na, ho - san - na in the high - est.

Tempo giusto

Celebrant Let us pro - claim the mys - t'ry of faith. *All* Christ has died, Christ is ri - sen;

Christ has died, Christ is ri - sen, Christ, Christ will come a - gain.

Tempo giusto

2

Celebrant Let us pro - claim the mys - t'ry of faith. *All* Dy - ing you des - troyed our death,

ris - ing you res - tored our life, Lord Je - sus. Come in glo - ry.

Tempo giusto

3

Celebrant Let us pro - claim the mys - t'ry of faith. *All* When we eat this bread, when we

drink this cup, we pro - claim your death Lord Je - sus, un - til you come in glo - ry.

Tempo giusto

4

Celebrant Let us pro - claim the mys - t'ry of faith. *All* Lord, by your cross and re - sur - rec - tion

you have set us free; you are the Sa - viour of the world.

GREAT AMEN

A - men, a - men, a - men, a - men.

OUR FATHER

Our Fa-ther, who art in hea-ven, hal-lowed be thy name: Thy king-dom come, thy

will be done on earth as it is in hea - ven. Give us this day our dai-ly bread; hal-lowed be thy

name: And for-give us our tres-pas-ses, as we for-give those who tres-pass a-gainst us.

And lead us not in - to temp-ta-tion; hal-lowed be thy name: But de-

liv-er us from e - vil, de - li-ver us from e - vil. Hal-lowed be thy name.

Celebrant: Deliver us, Lord, from every evil, and grant us peace in our day.
In your mercy, keep us free from sin and protect us from all anxiety
as we wait in joyful hope for the coming of our Saviour, Jesus Christ.

For the king-dom, the pow'r and the glo-ry are yours now and for e - ver. For the king-dom, the pow'r and the

glo - ry are yours now and for e - ver, for e - ver, for e - ver. A - men.

AGNUS DEI

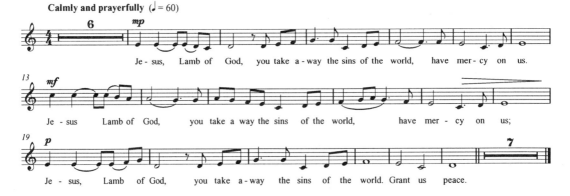

Je - sus, Lamb of God, you take a - way the sins of the world, have mer-cy on us.

Je - sus Lamb of God, you take a way the sins of the world, have mer - cy on us;

Je - sus, Lamb of God, you take a - way the sins of the world. Grant us peace.